rockschool®

Bass Grade 1

*Performance pieces, technical exercises and in-depth guidance
for Rockschool examinations*

www.rockschool.co.uk

Acknowledgements

Published by Rockschool Ltd. © 2012
Catalogue Number RSK051211
ISBN: 978-1-908920-10-2
Revision 1 | 9 November 2012 | Errata details can be found at *www.rockschool.co.uk*

AUDIO
Recorded at Fisher Lane Studios
Produced and engineered by Nick Davis
Assistant engineer and Pro Tools operator Mark Binge
Mixed and Mastered at Langlei Studios
Mixing and additional editing by Duncan Jordan
Supporting Tests recorded by Duncan Jordan and Kit Morgan
Mastered by Duncan Jordan
Executive producers: James Uings, Jeremy Ward and Noam Lederman

MUSICIANS
James Arben, Joe Bennett, Jason Bowld, Larry Carlton, Stuart Clayton, Andy Crompton, Neel Dhorajiwala, Fergus Gerrand,
Charlie Griffiths, Felipe Karam, Kishon Khan, Noam Lederman, DJ Harry Love, Dave Marks, Kit Morgan, Jon Musgrave,
Jake Painter, Richard Pardy, Ross Stanley, Stuart Ryan, Carl Sterling, Henry Thomas, Camilo Tirado, Simon Troup,
James Uings, Steve Walker, Chris Webster, Norton York, Nir Z

PUBLISHING
Fact Files written by Stuart Clayton
Walkthroughs written by Stuart Clayton
Music engraving and book layout by Simon Troup and Jennie Troup of Digital Music Art
Proof and copy editing by Stuart Clayton, Claire Davies, Stephen Lawson, Simon Pitt and James Uings
Publishing administration by Caroline Uings
Cover design by Philip Millard

SYLLABUS
Syllabus director: Jeremy Ward
Instrumental specialists: Stuart Clayton, Noam Lederman and James Uings
Special thanks to: Brad Fuller and Georg Voros

SPONSORSHIP
Noam Lederman plays Mapex Drums, PAISTE cymbals and uses Vic Firth Sticks
Rockschool would like to thank the following companies for donating instruments used in the cover artwork

PRINTING
Printed and bound in the United Kingdom by Caligraving Ltd
CDs manufactured in the European Union by Software Logistics

DISTRIBUTION
Exclusive Distributors: Music Sales Ltd

CONTACTING ROCKSCHOOL
www.rockschool.co.uk
Telephone: +44 (0)845 460 4747
Fax: +44 (0)845 460 1960

Table of Contents

Welcome to Rockschool Bass Grade 1

Welcome to Bass Grade 1
Welcome to the Rockschool Bass Grade 1 pack. This book and CD contain everything you need to play bass at this grade. In this book you will find the exam scores in both standard bass notation and TAB. The CD has full stereo mixes of each tune, backing tracks to play along to for practice, and spoken two bar count-ins to both the full mixes and the backing track versions of each of the songs.

Bass Exams
For each grade you have the option of taking one of two different types of examination:

- **Grade Exam:** a Grade Exam is a mixture of music performances, technical work and tests. You prepare three pieces (two of which may be Free Choice Pieces) and the contents of the Technical Exercise section. This accounts for 75% of the exam marks. The other 25% consists of: *either* a Sight Reading *or* an Improvisation & Interpretation test (10%), a pair of instrument specific Ear Tests (10%), and finally you will be asked five General Musicianship Questions (5%). The pass mark is 60%.

- **Performance Certificate:** in a Performance Certificate you play five pieces. Up to three of these can be Free Choice Pieces. Each song is marked out of 20 and the pass mark is 60%.

Book Contents
The book is divided into a number of sections:

- **Exam Pieces:** in this book you will find six specially commissioned pieces of Grade 1 standard. Each of these is preceded by a *Fact File*, and each single Fact File contains a summary of the song, its style, tempo, key and technical features, along with a list of the musicians who played on it. Also included is more in-depth information on the genre it is styled upon and relevant techniques you will encounter, as well as recommended further listening. The song itself is printed on two pages and immediately after each song is a *Walkthrough*. This covers the whole song from a performance perspective, focusing on the technical issues you will encounter along the way. Each Walkthrough features two graphical musical 'highlights' showing particular parts of the song. Each song comes with a full mix version and a backing track. Both versions have spoken count-ins at the beginning. Please note that any solos played on the full mix versions are indicative only.

- **Technical Exercises:** you should prepare the exercises set in this grade as indicated. There is also a Fill test that should be practised and played to the backing track.

- **Supporting Tests and General Musicianship Questions:** in Bass Grade 1 there are three supporting tests. You can choose *either* a Sight Reading test *or* an Improvisation & Interpretation test (please choose only one of those), which is then followed by the two mandatory Ear Tests and a set of General Musicianship Questions (GMQs). Examples of the types of tests likely to appear in the exam are printed in this book, while additional examples of both types of tests and the GMQs can be found in the Rockschool *Bass Companion Guide*.

- **Grade 2 Preview:** in this book we have included one of the songs featured in the Grade 2 Bass book as a taster. The piece is printed with its accompanying Fact File and Walkthrough, and the full mix and backing tracks are on the CD.

- **General Information:** finally, you will find the information you need on exam procedures, including online examination entry, marking schemes and what to do when arriving (and waiting) for your exam.

We hope you enjoy using this book. You will find a *Syllabus Guide* for Bass and other exam information on our website: *www.rockschool.co.uk*. Rockschool Graded Music Exams are accredited in England, Wales and Northern Ireland by Ofqual, the DfE and CCEA and by SQA Accreditation in Scotland.

SONG TITLE: CROSSTOWN LINK
GENRE: BLUES ROCK
TEMPO: 90 BPM
KEY: E MINOR

TECH FEATURES: EIGHTH-NOTE LINES
RESTS
DOTTED QUARTER NOTES

COMPOSER: ALISON RAYNER

PERSONNEL: STUART RYAN (GTR)
HENRY THOMAS (BASS)
NOAM LEDERMAN (DRUMS)

OVERVIEW

'Crosstown Link' is a blues rock track created in the style of artists such as legendary guitarist Jimi Hendrix, and popular rock bands of the 1960s-1970s including Cream (featuring Jack Bruce on bass) and Led Zeppelin (with bassist and keyboard player John Paul Jones). This period in rock history is considered a golden age for guitar heroes, but it was a creative time for bass players too. You will notice how the bassline featured in 'Crosstown Link' is an active one, comprised of a strong groove peppered with a variety of fills throughout.

STYLE FOCUS

Essentially, the blues rock style is based on blues chord progressions played with a hard rock edge. The guitar is the focal point here, and it was during the mid 1960s that Hendrix popularized the use of feedback and wildly overdriven guitars. This style of blues rock was extravagant and essentially enabled bass players to move away from the more traditional walking basslines and indulge in riffs, fills and improvised lines. A common blues rock bassline will feature riff based groove sections, chromatic lines (which involve connecting chords and adding tension), plus improvised fills.

THE BIGGER PICTURE

Blues rock developed in Britain and America during the 1960s. It began as the blues played with a harder edge then evolved as musicians experimented by adding new chords and extra sections to the traditional 12-bar structure. Improvisations in the style were originally centred on jazz lines before moving towards heavier, riff driven ideas based on pentatonic scales. It was during this time that many of today's well known guitarists, including Eric Clapton, Hendrix, Jimmy Page and John Mayall, made their mark. Bass icons emerged too, including the aforementioned Jack Bruce and John Paul Jones, as well as Noel Redding (The Jimi Hendrix Experience), John Entwistle (The Who) and Andy Fraser (Free). Blues rock is still popular today and has been carried on by the likes of Joe Bonamassa, John Mayer, The White Stripes and Them Crooked Vultures.

RECOMMENDED LISTENING

Classic Hendrix tracks 'Fire', 'Crosstown Traffic' and 'Purple Haze' are great jumping off points. The John Mayall album *Blues Breakers With Eric Clapton* (1966), also known as the 'Beano album' (the cover pictured Clapton reading a copy of the Beano) is a great example, as is Cream's *Wheels Of Fire* (1968).

Crosstown Link

Alison Rayner

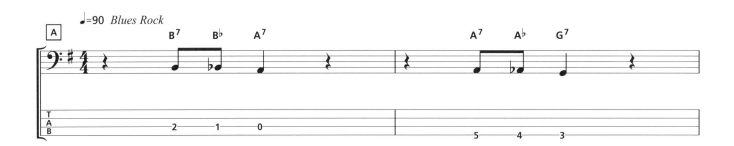

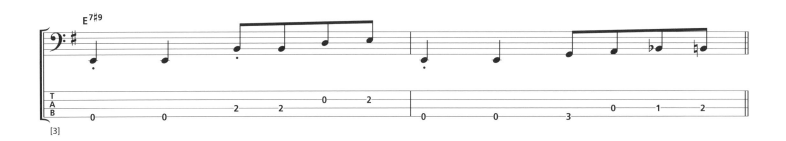

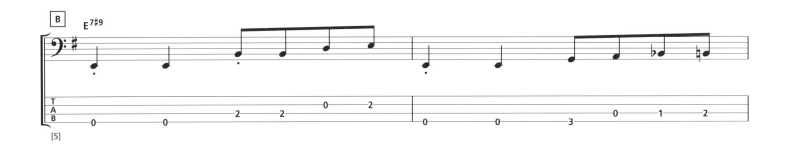

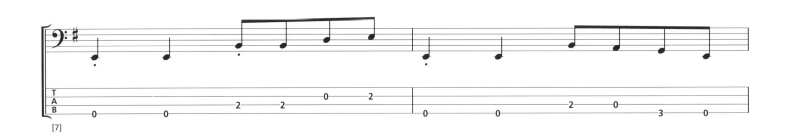

[11]

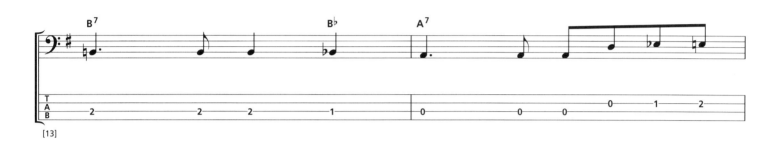

[13]

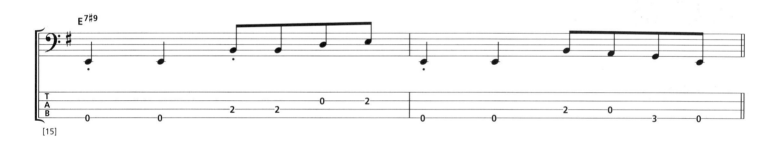

[15]

[17]

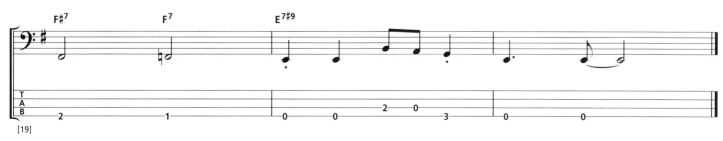

[19]

Bass Grade 1

Walkthrough

A Section (Bars 1–4)
The first four bars of 'Crosstown Link' feature the use of quarter-note rests on the first beat of the bar, plus the introduction of the main riff.

Bars 1–21 | *Staccato Notes*
There are many staccato notes (marked with a dot) in 'Crosstown Link'. These should be articulated by releasing pressure on the string. Don't take the finger all the way off the string, this will slow you down and may produce unwanted string noise, just stop pressing.

Bars 1–2 | *Quarter note rests*
In the first two bars of this section, rests are used for the first beat of the bar. You should take care not to play on beat one, which is tempting after a "1–2–3–4" count-in (Fig. 1).

Bars 1–2 | *Chromatic notes*
Both of these two bars contain a three note descending chromatic line (to move chromatically means to move directly to the next fret). Any time there is chromatic movement in a song, there will be accidentals in the notation – you can see a B♭ in the first bar and an A♭ in the second. Even though these notes do not occur naturally in the key, they add plenty of weight when used between the notes that do belong to the key.

Bar 3 | *The main riff*
The main 'Crosstown Link' riff is introduced in the third bar (Fig. 2), and consists of two quarter notes on the low E string, followed by four eighth notes on the last two beats. Count these eighth notes evenly to ensure they are of the same length.

B Section (Bars 5–16)
The B section of this song follows the standard 12-bar blues structure and is based around the riff introduced during the final two bars of the A section.

Bar 6 | *Riff variation*
In this bar you will see a variation of the main riff that is used at several points within the piece. After playing the two quarter note E notes, the group of four eighth notes starts on the G at the third fret of the E string before ascending chromatically from the open A to the B♭ and finally to the B. To play this cleanly, fret the G with your third finger and the B♭ and B with your first and second fingers.

Bars 9–10 | *Moving the riff*
In these bars the main riff is moved onto the A string. Bar 10 contains a variation on this riff: after the first eighth note E, an open G is played followed by E and D notes on the D string. When playing this, take care to mute the open G with your fret hand after playing it to prevent it from ringing on into the next beat.

Bars 13–14 | *Dotted quarter notes*
In these bars you will discover dotted quarter notes. Dotted notes extend the value of a note by 50 per cent. so that the dotted quarter note then lasts for a beat and a half. To accomplish this, play the first B on beat one and the second on the '&' of beat two. Make sure that the first note rings until the second one is played.

C Section (Bars 17–21)
This final section is similar to the intro and contains the same chromatic figures that start on the second beat.

Bar 19 | *Half notes*
In this bar, two half notes are played. You will need to play the first note on beat one and play the second on beat three.

Bar 21 | *Use of a tie*
In the final bar, the dotted quarter-note rhythm appears again. The second note is played on the upbeat (or '&') of beat two, and in the notation you discover how this is connected to the final half note with a tie. This means that when you play the note on the upbeat of beat two, you should allow it to ring for the duration of the note it is tied to without re-playing it.

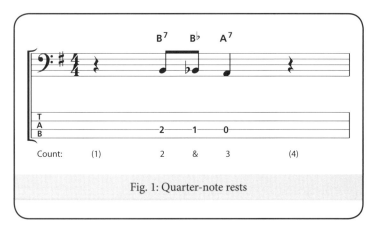

Fig. 1: Quarter-note rests

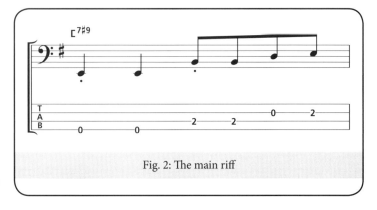

Fig. 2: The main riff

SONG TITLE: NIGHT RIDE

GENRE: ROCK

TEMPO: 120 BPM

KEY: A MAJOR

TECH FEATURES: EIGHTH-NOTE GROOVES

RESTS

OPEN STRINGS

COMPOSER: SIMON TROUP

PERSONNEL: STUART RYAN (GTR)

HENRY THOMAS (BASS)

NOAM LEDERMAN (DRUMS)

OVERVIEW

Kings Of Leon, The Script, Foo Fighters and Stereophonics are renowned for their dynamic rock songs, and 'Night Ride' takes its cue from them. The bassline begins in a simple manner using root notes and basic rhythms to underpin the chords. As the song progresses, the bassline gradually evolves with more fills and rhythmic elements introduced. As per most rock songs, 'Night Ride' can be played either with a pick or with the fingers. The important thing to remember is to play the line with consistency.

STYLE FOCUS

Rock is a wide ranging term that encompasses many other musical genres. The focus is usually on the guitar and vocals, with bass guitar and drums playing supportive roles. Rock basslines vary enormously throughout rock, with some bands favouring repetitive eighth-note based lines yet others opting for a more melodic walking bass approach. Technical proficiency is valued more highly than in some other styles of music, such as punk, for example, but by far the most important thing is that the bass supports the song without dominating it.

THE BIGGER PICTURE

Rock music first emerged in Britain and America in the 1960s and was initially a mixture of blues and rock 'n' roll. In the following two decades rock divided into numerous sub-genres: blues rock, punk rock, indie rock, progressive rock and more. All of these were dominated by a focus on the electric guitar and commonly used a basic format of bass, drums, guitar and vocals. Keyboards and piano were also used, especially in prog. Most rock songs followed a basic verse-chorus structure, typically incorporating a guitar solo in the second half of the song. Rock is still a dominant force in the charts and contemporary bands Kings of Leon and Foo Fighters, to name just two, are playing sold out stadium tours, headlining major festivals and releasing world-beating albums under the rock banner.

RECOMMENDED LISTENING

We have already mentioned Kings of Leon – check out their album *Only By The Night* (2008), and Foo Fighters *The Colour And The Shape* (1997), but rock forefathers AC/DC also have a thrilling back catalogue, especially *Back In Black* (1980).

Night Ride

Simon Troup

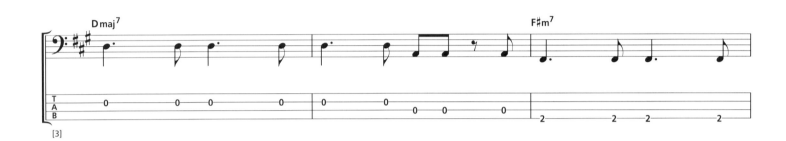

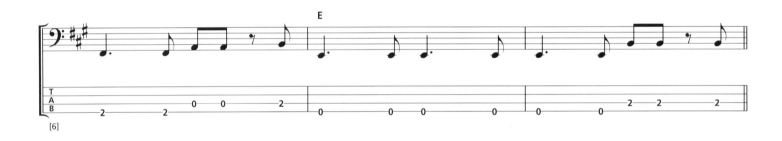

[15]

[17]

[20]

[23]

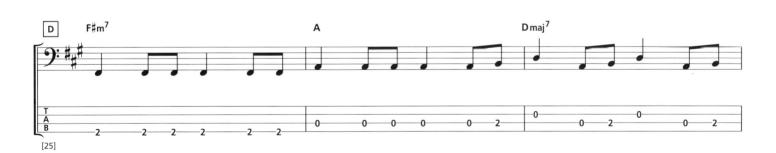

[25]

[28]

Walkthrough

A Section (Bars 1–8)
The song starts with an eight bar verse, and the bassline is a simple part using root notes to outline the chords.

Bars 1–40 | *Locking in with the drums*
Listen closely to the kick drum and snare hits and try to match your part to the rhythm track. You won't always be playing on the same beats as the drums, but the two parts should fit together in a complementary way.

Bar 1 | *Dotted quarter notes and eighth notes*
The basic rhythm for this verse section is a dotted quarter note followed by an eighth note. This rhythm is used twice here. To play this rhythm, play the first note on the first beat and the next note on the upbeat or '&' of the second beat.

Bars 1–4 | *Counting rhythms*
You should find most of the rhythms in this section quite easy to pick up aurally. If you struggle with any of them, try counting the bar in eighth notes ("1 & 2 & 3 & 4 &") and work out where each note falls. Practise the phrase slowly, gradually increasing speed as you become more comfortable.

B Section (Bars 9–16)
The second verse follows the same chord progression as the first, but here the bassline is busier.

Bar 10 | *Using the fifth*
In this bar, the bass moves up to the fifth of the A chord rather than remaining on the root note. The fifth (an E note) is a great note choice for bass players in all styles of music. Here it works for two reasons: it is a strong note in the A chord and it leads nicely to the D chord in the following bar.

Bar 12 | *Melodic link*
There is a melodic link on the third and fourth beats of this bar. Rather than staying on the root note D the bass moves up to the E and is followed by an F♮, which makes for a great transition into the next bar.

Bar 14 | *Using the minor third*
Now the bass moves from the root note of the F♯m⁷ chord up to the minor third, which is an A at the 2nd fret of the G string (Fig. 1). This note gives the chord its 'minor' quality, and leads directly to the G♯ in the following bar.

Bar 15 | *Using the major third*
The minor third (A) played in the previous bar leads directly to the G♯ in this bar. The G♯ is the major third of the E chord played by the guitar and is the note that gives the chord its major quality. The idea of using major and minor thirds in the bassline is a popular one, but the third does not sound as strong as the root and fifth so it is not used as often.

C Section (Bars 17–24)
A different feel is used for this section, and the bassline contains a lot of rests as well as some melodic passages that connect the chords.

Bar 17 | *Eighth-note rests*
As the chorus section arrives, the bass plays a different rhythmic idea. One eighth note is played on each beat, but because each is an eighth note followed by an eighth note rest they should be kept short.

Bar 20 | *Melodic bass fill*
There is another melodic bass fill in this bar, linking the C♯m⁷ and F♯m⁷ chords (Fig. 2). Here the bass walks downwards from the C♯ through notes that belong to the key, arriving neatly at the F♯ at the beginning of the next bar.

D Section (Bars 25–30)
The final section of this song features a busy quarter note and eighth note bassline involving string crossing.

Bars 27–29 | *Muting*
In these three identical bars, you are required to play the open D string followed by the open A string. Make sure that you mute the open D with your fretting hand fingers as you move to the A string.

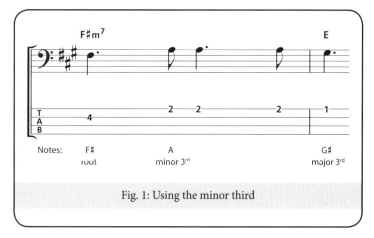

Fig. 1: Using the minor third

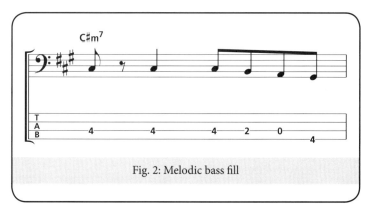

Fig. 2: Melodic bass fill

SONG TITLE: RELUCTANT HERO

GENRE: GRUNGE

TEMPO: 115 BPM

KEY: E MINOR

TECH FEATURES: EIGHTH NOTE GROOVES
RESTS
STRING CROSSING

COMPOSER: JAMES UINGS

PERSONNEL: STUART RYAN (GTR)
HENRY THOMAS (BASS)
NOAM LEDERMAN (DRUMS)

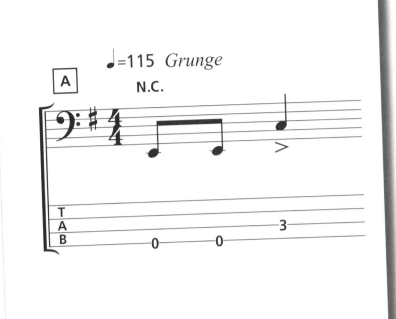

OVERVIEW

'Reluctant Hero' is a grunge track written in the style of the bands Nirvana, Soundgarden, Alice In Chains and Pearl Jam. It features rests and string crossing among its techniques. A common motif in grunge is that the bass doubles the guitar on chorus sections and big riffs, then holds down an eighth-note based groove during the verse sections. As with any style of music it is important to be solid and supportive here, but you should also play with a sense of authority in order to capture the grunge sound in its true form.

STYLE FOCUS

Grunge has never been about technical ability or complexity. Instead it is a style of music based on simple ideas performed with feeling and to a high standard. Grunge tracks often feature an obvious use of dynamics, with the idea of 'quiet verse, loud chorus' being a common template. Grunge basslines are often simple, but timing and accuracy are just as important here as in any other style of music. A typical grunge bassline can be played either with the fingers or a plectrum, but a thick, meaty tone is essential in order to anchor the piece throughout both the big riffs and the more subdued sections.

THE BIGGER PICTURE

Grunge is a sub genre of rock music that developed in the local punk scene in and around the American city of Seattle during the late 1980s and early 1990s. It emerged partly as a reaction to the overblown theatrical rock music of the 1980s and defined itself more through song dynamics and lyrical content than technical guitar playing or extravagant shows. Grunge bands adopted an entirely different look to conventional rock bands and spiked the interest of youths disconnected from mainstream music. Grunge became a phenomenon thanks largely to the release of two albums in 1991: *Nevermind* by Nirvana and *Ten* by Pearl Jam.

RECOMMENDED LISTENING

Nevermind is the quintessential grunge album, containing 'Lithium', 'Come As You Are' and 'Smells Like Teen Spirit'. *Ten*, Pearl Jam's debut, yielded the instant classics 'Alive', 'Jeremy' and 'Even Flow'. During the grunge movement that sprang off the back of Nirvana and Pearl Jam's success, Soundgarden (listen to 'Spoonman' and 'Black Hole Sun') and Alice in Chains ('Them Bones' and 'Down in a Hole') opened the floodgates for more obscure bands through the definitive grunge record label Subpop.

Reluctant Hero

James Uings

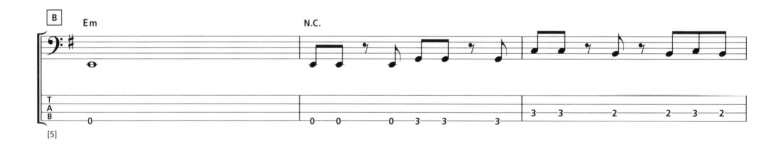

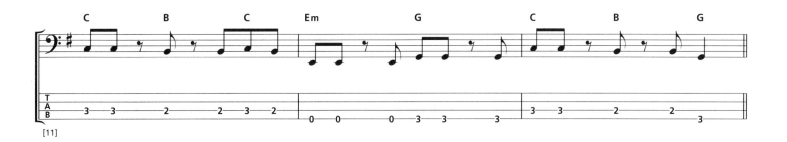

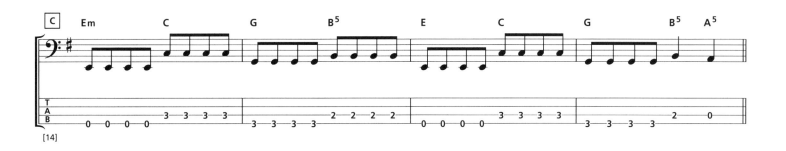

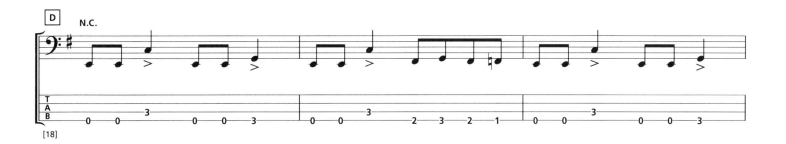

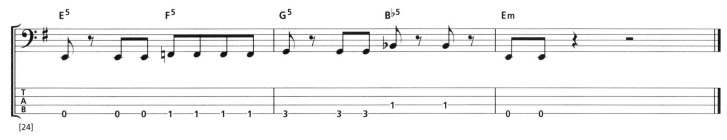

Walkthrough

A Section (Bars 1–4)

The opening four bars of 'Reluctant Hero' feature a powerful riff played in unison with the guitar which is reused later in the song as the second half of the D section.

Bar 1 | *Quarter notes and eighth notes*

This part of the song is built on two different rhythms of quarter notes and eighth notes. The first and third beats of bar 1 have two eighth notes (both played on the open E string) followed by a quarter note C on the second beat and a quarter note G on the fourth. This rhythm emphasises the second and fourth beats, thus adding weight and power to the riff (Fig. 1).

Bar 2 | *Accidentals*

In this bar you will see a natural sign next to the F in the notation. This is used because the key signature dictates that all Fs should be played as F♯. Due to the F natural needed here, the natural sign is used. This note is part of a chromatic descending riff, which is a popular device in grunge music.

Bars 1–4 | *Playing in unison*

These bars are played in unison with the rhythm guitar, so listen carefully and try to match your part closely.

B Section (Bars 5–13)

The B section of this song features a shift in dynamic so it is quieter and leaves space for a vocal line. The first bar contains a whole note that helps to establish the new section, and this is followed by eight bars of an eighth-note groove.

Bar 5 | *Whole note*

In bar 5 you will play a whole note lasting for four beats. Make sure that you play this note with enough attack for it to last the full duration.

Bars 6–13 | *Eighth-note groove*

This section of the song features an eighth-note groove with rests on the beginning of the second and fourth beats (Fig. 2). Take time to master this rhythm because it is used in many styles of music. To begin, try playing continuous eighth notes through the section at first then leave out the first note on the second and fourth beats, playing only on the offbeat. You should find that this enhances the feel of the line. It is important that the rests are observed here.

Bars 6–13 | *String crossing*

The eighth-note line used in this section is played on both the E and A strings. Switching between strings is one of the hardest things to do accurately on the bass, so approach this line carefully. You can use either of your hands to mute strings as you switch, but you really need to ensure that neither string continues to ring as you switch to the next.

C Section (Bars 14–17)

This section is a continuous eighth-note line used to build excitement as the track approaches the big D section.

Bars 14–16 | *Continuous eighth notes*

Throughout this section you will be playing continuous eighth notes, comprising of two notes per beat. In order for this to sound authentic, play with an even attack and lock in closely with the drums. To lock in tightly, listen carefully to the placement of the kick and snare drums.

D Section (Bars 18–26)

This is the biggest, most powerful section of the tune. The first four bars are the same as the A section, while the second four bars act as the closing section to the song.

Bar 23 | *Accidentals*

In this bar you will come across another accidental in the notation called a B♭. Accidentals are notes that occur outside the key of the song and can be highly effective at creating tension in riffs such as this one.

Bars 22–26 | *Riffing with the guitar*

This is an exciting section where you will once again double the guitar riff. This part is loud and powerful, so don't be afraid to dig in. While doing so, remember to lock in your part precisely with the guitar to avoid rushing.

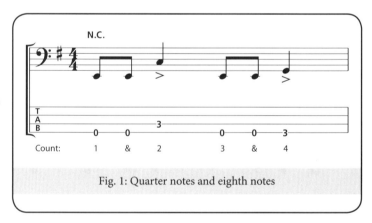

Fig. 1: Quarter notes and eighth notes

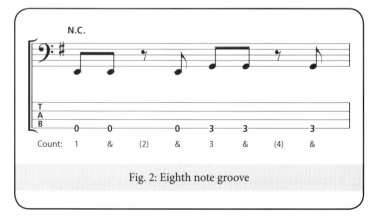

Fig. 2: Eighth note groove

SONG TITLE: KRAUSS COUNTRY
GENRE: COUNTRY
TEMPO: 88 BPM
KEY: D MAJOR

TECH FEATURES: STRING CROSSING
EIGHTH NOTE GROOVES
RESTS

COMPOSER: DEIRDRE CARTWRIGHT

PERSONNEL: STUART RYAN (GTR)
HENRY THOMAS (BASS)
NOAM LEDERMAN (DRUMS)

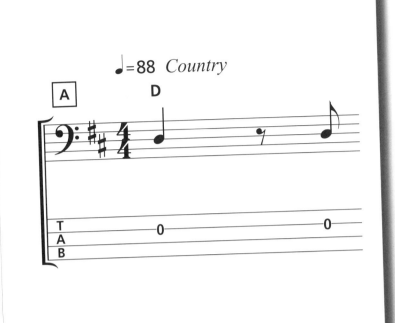

OVERVIEW

'Krauss Country' is a gentle country bluegrass piece that brings to mind artists like Alison Krauss, Carrie Underwood and Taylor Swift. The song also tips its hat to classic bluegrass players Lester Flatt and Earl Scruggs, Patty Loveless and Bill Monroe. The bass guitar plays an important role in all styles of country and often switches between the root note and the fifth of the chord being played.

STYLE FOCUS

Many country songs use simple diatonic chord progressions. A diatonic chord progression is one in which only the chords that occur naturally in the key are used. Although instrumentation varies greatly in country, it consists mainly of acoustic guitars, bass, drums and vocals. However, harmonica, banjo, mandolin and fiddle are also popular. The bass plays a supportive role in country music, supplying a solid foundation for the melody and vocals.

THE BIGGER PICTURE

The roots of country music go back to the southern states of America in the 19th Century, when various European folk traditions merged into an acoustic style known today as old timey or hillbilly. While country began as a form of local entertainment, the style enjoyed widespread popularity throughout the 20th Century with Elvis Presley and Johnny Cash enjoying country hits in the 1960s. The genre continues to be popular today with Taylor Swift and Carrie Underwood flying the flag and, in Swift's case, adding a mainstream, chart friendly pop edge.

Bluegrass became popular towards the middle of the last century and was a refined form of the old timey style. Lester Flatt and Earl Scruggs did as much as anyone to raise its profile. Today the genre is exemplified by the band Union Station.

RECOMMENDED LISTENING

Artists such as Johnny Cash, Garth Brooks, Dolly Parton and Willie Nelson are all huge country music stars and have recorded tens of albums with a strong country flavour. Taylor Swift and Alison Krauss have also scored big with 'Love Story' and 'Down To The River To Pray', respectively. Finally, 'Reunion In Heaven' and 'Same Old Day' by Lester Flatt and Earl Scruggs will educate you on the elements of bluegrass that can be heard in the piece which you will learn over the next few pages.

Krauss Country

Deirdre Cartwright

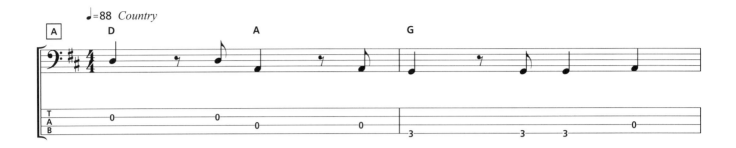

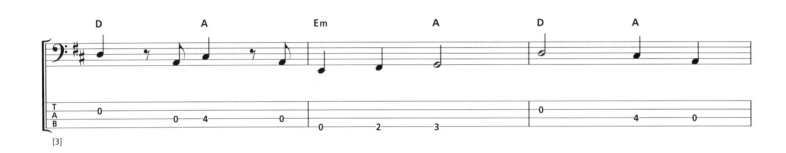

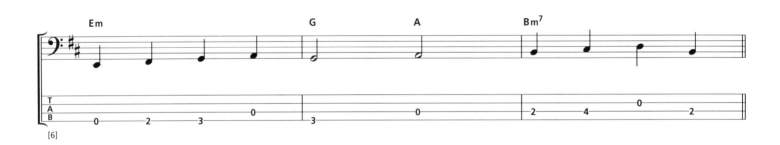

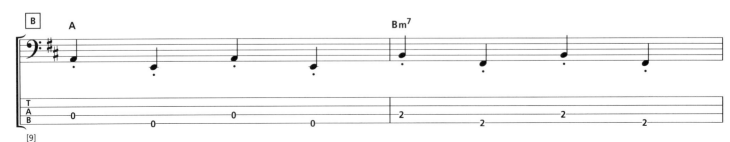

18

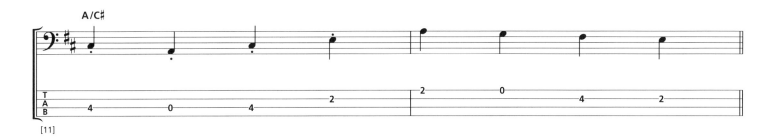

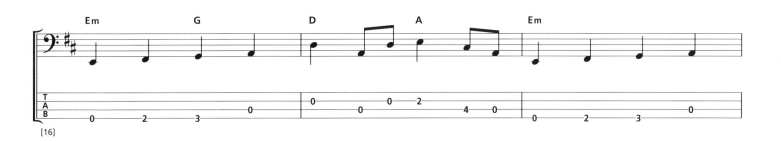

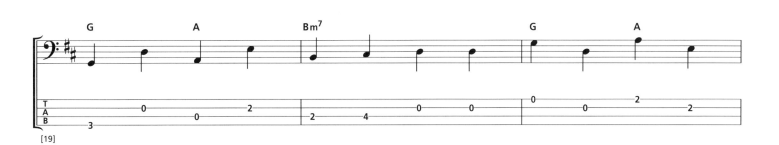

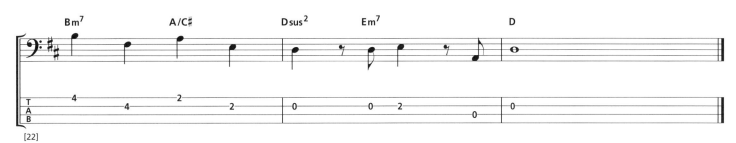

Bass Grade 1

19

Walkthrough

A Section (Bars 1–8)
The A section of 'Krauss Country' features a simple bassline that utilises a variety of different rhythms.

Bars 1–3 | *Quarter note and eighth-note line*
This bar features a line built on a quarter note and eighth note figure, with a rest on the first part of the second beat (Fig. 1). When tackling this, play the first D on beat one and the second D on the upbeat (the second half or "&" count) of beat two. The first part of beat two should be a rest. This rhythmic figure, used in a wide variety of genres, is then repeated on an A note for the third and fourth beats.

Bars 1–4 | *String crossing*
The first four bars contain a lot of string crossing and the use of open strings. When moving between open strings, it is important to mute them to stop them from ringing into one another. You can do this by bringing in your fretting hand to mute the string or by using your picking hand fingers.

Bars 5–8 | *Relaxed feel*
While the whole of this piece should be played with a relaxed feel, this is particularly important in these bars. After playing the half note and quarter notes in bar 5, be careful not to rush ahead of the beat when playing the ascending line in bar 6 (Fig. 2).

B Section (Bars 9–12)
The verse section of this song features a different feel for the first three bars. Longer note values are used here to create a different mood and you will discover some new combinations of rests too.

Bars 9–10 | *Root and fifth*
In these two bars, the bassline uses a common musical device of moving between the root note and the fifth of the chord. In this instance, the fifth is played below the root note. You can see this clearly in bar 10 where the B on the A string is the root of the chord, while the F♯ on the E string is the fifth of the chord.

Bar 12 | *Descending line*
The end of this section features an ascending bassline that moves downwards from A, which is the root note, allowing the line to begin on a D in the next bar. This ascending line brings the verse section to a close and creates a nice transition into the chorus.

C Section (Bars 13–24)
This section of the song reintroduces many elements that featured earlier in the piece, but look out for the faster rhythms that appear here.

Bar 16 | *Ascending line*
An ascending quarter note bassline is employed here to support the chords E minor and G. The notes on beats one and three are the root notes of these chords, while the notes on beats two and four are passing notes used to create a sense of movement in the line.

Bar 17 | *Quarter notes and eighth notes*
This bar contains a combination of quarter notes and eighth notes. As you count through the bar, play one note on beats one and three, and two evenly spaced notes on beats two and four. You can practise this rhythm using one note to begin with before adding the correct notes.

Bars 21–22 | *Two note sequences*
There are two notes for each chord change here: the root and fifth. When playing these, remember that muting is required while crossing strings in order for the line to sound clean.

Bars 25–28 | *Outro*
This final passage brings the song to a close and features more root–fifth movement from the bass.

Bar 28 | *Whole note*
This piece ends with a whole note that lasts for four beats. You will need to play this note with sufficient attack for it to ring clearly throughout the bar. Try not to cut the note off too early and allow it to ring for the full four beats.

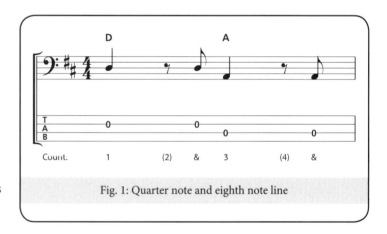

Fig. 1: Quarter note and eighth note line

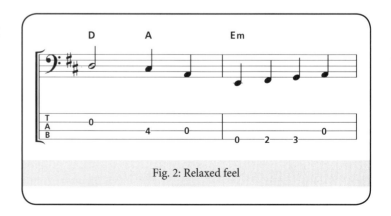

Fig. 2: Relaxed feel

SONG TITLE: THE OPEN AIR

GENRE: MODERN ROCK

TEMPO: 80 BPM

KEY: F♯ MINOR

TECH FEATURES: STRING CROSSING

TIED NOTES

TIMING

COMPOSER: DAVE MARKS

PERSONNEL: STUART RYAN (GTR)

HENRY THOMAS (BASS)

NOAM LEDERMAN (DRUMS)

OVERVIEW

As a step on from our previous rock tune 'Night Ride', here we focus on bands including the power trios Biffy Clyro and Muse, as well as stadium headliners The Killers, all of whom have added a modern slant to rock. 'The Open Air' is a piece in the style of all three bands and will give you a taster of playing within a modern rock format. Modern rock has taken inspiration from many sub-genres of rock that have gone before and includes textures of other styles of music too. As a result, it is not unusual for the bassist to have an interesting role to play in the band. Modern rock music often mixes huge riffs, odd time signatures and various effects, and can feature many idioms of bass playing from fingerstyle and pick playing to slapping and chord playing.

STYLE FOCUS

The role of the bass player in a modern rock group is far less predefined than in classic rock. This means bassists have the freedom to play with more unconventional techniques, experiment with an extended range of instruments, such as five string bass guitars, and explore different effects pedals. While modern rock basslines can certainly be simple, there is also scope for far more complex parts.

THE BIGGER PICTURE

Modern rock generally refers to any rock music recorded from the late 1990s through to the present day. It provides a contrast to classic rock, which mostly covers rock music recorded before this period (think Def Leppard and Van Halen). Modern rock can mix elements from progressive rock, funk, reggae, punk and even classical music. These elements mean that the music is often more complex than classic rock, with far more opportunities for the bassist to create interesting lines. Modern rock bassists Chris Wolstenholme (Muse), Mark Stoermer (The Killers), and James Johnston (Biffy Clyro) are examples of bassists who create inventive, melodic lines.

RECOMMENDED LISTENING

There are many modern rock bands worth listening to, but some of the most desirable from a bassist's point of view are the aforementioned as well as Queens Of The Stone Age. Muse songs 'New Born' and 'Plug In Baby' showcase Chris Wolstenholme's complex effects-led lines, while 'Mr. Brightside' and 'Somebody Told Me' show off The Killers' Mark Stoermer's melodic playing. Biffy Clyro's James Johnston should be heard in action on the top 10 chart hits 'Mountains' and 'The Captain'.

The Open Air

Tracks 9 & 10

Dave Marks

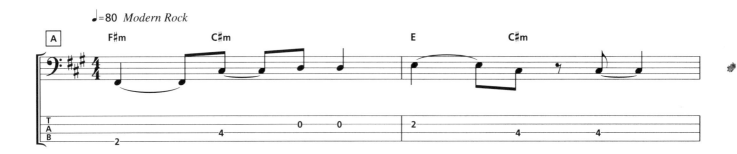

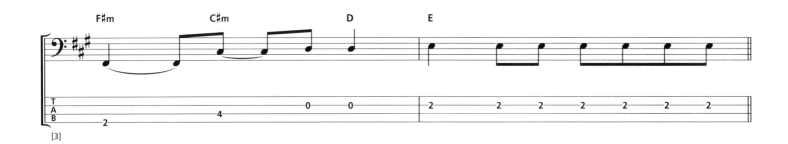

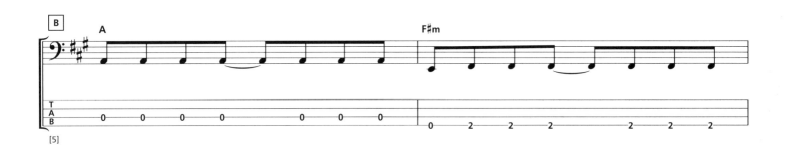

Bass Grade 1

22

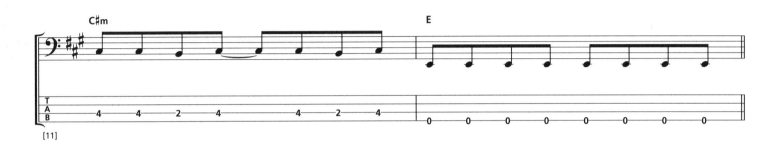

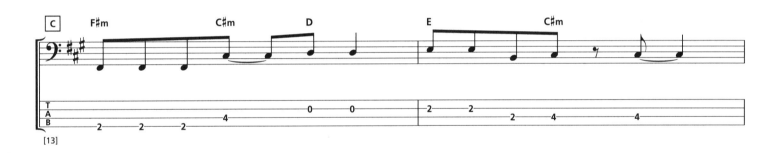

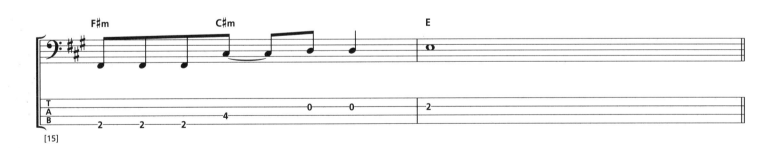

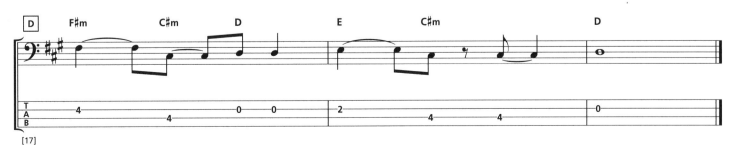

Walkthrough

A Section (Bars 1–4)
The first four bars of this piece form the intro section, which contains some unusual timings.

Bar 1 | *Tied notes*
The first bar features a quarter note and eighth note rhythm that includes some tied notes. A tie connects two notes together, meaning that only the first note is played, but it then lasts for the duration of the first note and the note it is tied to. Here you will find that the first note lasts for a quarter note and an eighth note. The second note is therefore played on the upbeat of beat two, with the third note played on the upbeat of beat three. The final note is played on beat four.

Bars 1–3 | *Timing*
The use of ties in this bassline creates a slightly unusual rhythmic pattern that will require some practice in order for you to perform it correctly. The important thing to remember when playing this line is that each beat can be divided into two eighth notes. Try to count "1 & 2 & 3 & 4" throughout the bar, keeping each note the same length (Fig. 1). You can then focus on the beats (or upbeats) where the notes are played.

Bars 1–19 | *Fretting accuracy*
A combination of open strings and fretted notes is used throughout this piece. It is important that all of the notes sound even and last for their full duration. When playing fretted notes, be sure to place your left hand finger in the centre of the fret to get a clean note. If your finger is too close to the metal fretwire you are likely to create fretbuzz.

B Section (Bars 5–12)
This section of the song is eight bars long and based around an eighth note rhythm that uses tied notes.

Bars 5–12 | *Playing evenly*
Throughout this section, you will be playing an almost continuous eighth-note bassline (Fig. 2). When playing lines such as this, it is crucial to play evenly. If you are playing with your fingers as opposed to a pick, you should concentrate on playing with the same part of each finger – the soft pad on the fingertip – and keeping the volume and attack the same from finger to finger.

Bars 5–8 | *Tied notes*
A much simpler rhythm using ties is introduced in the verse section. Now you will play an almost continuous eighth-note groove throughout the bar, making the fourth note last until the upbeat (or '&') of the third beat. This is the note that is tied in the notation. When playing this line, play a note on every beat and upbeat except for beat three.

Bar 8 | *Bass fill*
In bar 8 there is a short bass fill. This consists of three descending notes used to enable a smooth transition from the E in the eighth bar to the A at the beginning of the ninth. As the bassline has been the same all the way through the verse up until this point, this simple fill provides some variety to the line.

C Section (Bars 13–16)
This part of the song is similar to the intro but with more movement in the bassline.

Bar 13 | *Added notes*
The bassline in this bar follows the same chord changes as the first bar of the intro but with added notes. Here, three F♯'s are played before the C♯ on the upbeat of bar 2. This note is then tied across to the third beat, and the D is played on the upbeat of beat three and on beat four.

D Section (Bars 17–19)
The final section of 'The Open Air' is a variation of the first two bars of the piece and finishes with a D whole note.

Bar 19 | *Note lengths*
It can be tempting to let the final note ring on for longer than notated. Make sure you stop it after four beats.

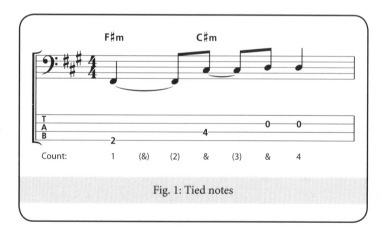

Fig. 1: Tied notes

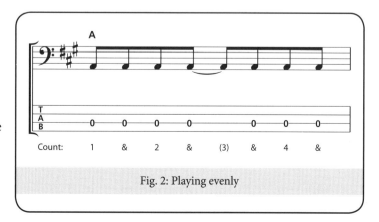

Fig. 2: Playing evenly

SONG TITLE: INSIDE THE BOX

GENRE: SURF ROCK

TEMPO: 120 BPM

KEY: C MAJOR

TECH FEATURES: STACCATO NOTES

ACCIDENTALS

RESTS

COMPOSER: JOE BENNETT

PERSONNEL: STUART RYAN (GTR)

HENRY THOMAS (BASS)

NOAM LEDERMAN (DRUMS)

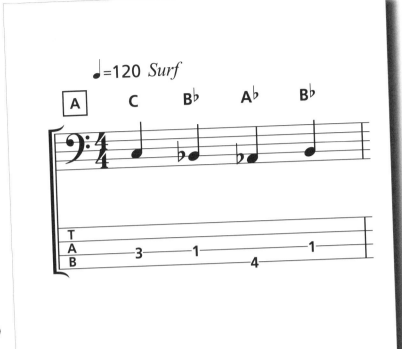

OVERVIEW

1960s surf rock groups such as Dick Dale and The Del-Tones (also known as His Del-Tones), The Surfaris and The Beach Boys have inspired 'Inside The Box'. As with most styles of rock, surf rock focused on the electric guitar. Even so, the bass player's role in this genre is far from dull. You will often find yourself doubling guitar riffs, playing melodic walking lines and marking accents with the drums, all the while maintaining a solid foundation for the band.

STYLE FOCUS

Surf rock evolved in the early 1960s as a form of instrumental rock 'n' roll. Lead guitar was often the dominant instrument, although saxophones were also popular. During this time the bass guitar was in its infancy, and many surf rock bass parts were derived from the walking basslines found on early rock 'n' roll records. Basic chord progressions were favoured in surf rock, often played at fast tempos.

THE BIGGER PICTURE

Instrumental rock was popular in the early 1960s thanks to artists such as Duane Eddy and Link Wray, and later evolved into surf rock through artists such as The Bel-Airs and Dick Dale. Dale is frequently credited with pioneering the use of spring reverb in the genre, as well as introducing fast tremolo picking to add a Mexican meets Spanish flourish.

Dale's hit song 'Misirlou' (which enjoyed a resurgence in popularity after its use in the movie *Pulp Fiction*) is a perfect example. While many surf rock songs were instrumental, vocal groups became popular and scored the biggest hits during that period. The Beach Boys were riding high with 'Surfin' Safari' and 'Surfin' USA', and were the only group to outlast the surf rock craze and enjoy success with *Pet Sounds* (1966) and other albums.

RECOMMENDED LISTENING

The key surf rock artists are Dick Dale and The Del-Tones, The Surfaris and The Beach Boys. Dick Dale tracks including 'Misirlou' and 'King Of The Surf Guitar' will pique your interest in surf rock, while 'Wipe Out' by The Surfaris is one of the most famous genre instrumentals of all time. In addition to those mentioned earlier, The Beach Boys' classic 'I Get Around', 'California Girls' and 'Sloop John B' will provide you with an excellent insight into more vocal-based surf rock.

Inside The Box

Joe Bennett

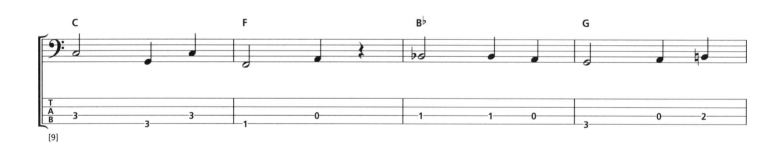

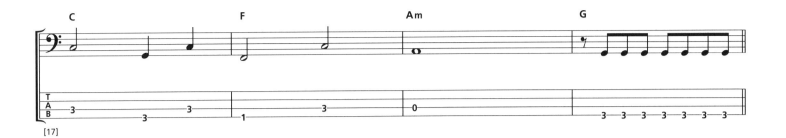

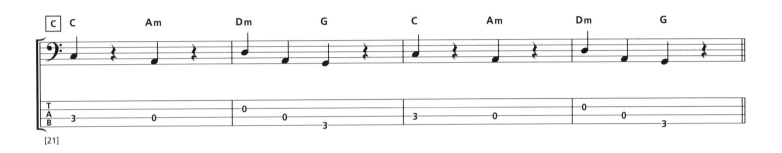

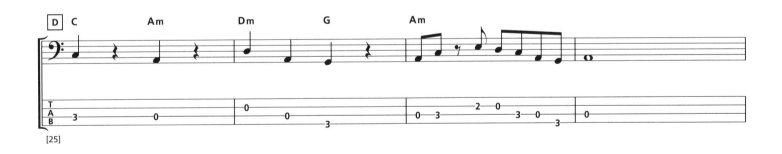

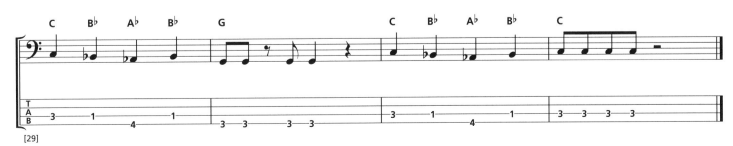

Bass Grade 1

27

Walkthrough

A Section (Bars 1–4)
The first four bars of this piece are a unison riff played on the guitar, and this particular riff features a firmly established surf rock sound.

Bar 1 | *Accidentals*
Three of the notes in the first bar, B♭, A♭ and B♭ again, do not belong to the key of this piece. Note how the second B♭ does not need a flat symbol because the one used earlier lasts for the whole bar (Fig. 1). When playing these, fret the C on the A string with your third finger, the B♭ on the same string with your first finger, and the A♭ on the E string with your fourth finger.

Bar 2 | *Eighth-note rest*
In the second bar, an eighth note rest is used on the first part of the second beat. After playing the two eighth notes on the first beat, the third note you play should fall on the '&' of the second beat. Count "1 & 2 & 3 & 4 &" throughout the bar to get a feel for how eighth notes should sound.

Bar 4 | *Staccato notes*
This bar contains a quarter note marked with a staccato dot beneath the notehead. This tells you to play the note short and detached rather than letting it ring for a full beat. When playing the note, aim to shorten it by lifting your fretting hand finger from the string slightly.

B Section (Bars 5–20)
This is the longest section of the track and features a lead guitar melody. You will hear how the bass guitar underpins this melody with a simple quarter-note line built from notes found in the chords.

Bars 5–19 | *Half and quarter note lines*
Throughout this section the bass plays quarter notes with rests occasionally used on the fourth beat. Although these are simple to count, the key to making this line sound good is to ensure that the rests are played *as rests* and that none of the notes ring into them.

Bars 11–12 | *Notation for accidentals*
In bar 11, you will see that another accidental, a B♭, is used. As before, this applies to the entire bar. You can see that in bar 12 a natural sign has been included before the B (Fig. 2). Even though the flat from bar 11 only applies in that bar, a natural sign is often used in the following bar as a reminder that the note is played as a natural and not a flat.

Bar 20 | *Eighth-note build*
This bar consists of an eighth-note rest followed by seven eighth notes. Practise this bar by playing an entire bar of eighth notes (two per beat), before leaving out the first one.

Remember that the first note you play should fall on the upbeat of the first beat.

C Section (Bars 21–24)
The C section consists of a repeating two bar figure before a final two bar tag leads the piece into the D section.

Bar 22 | *Open strings*
Two open strings used in this bar are played in a descending order. Ensure you mute the open D string with your left hand when moving to play the open A string.

Bar 27 | *Eighth-note line*
Aside from the rest on the first part of the second beat, this is a full bar of eighth notes. After playing the first two notes, play the next five notes starting on the '&' of beat two.

D Section (Bars 25–32)
This section is a reprise of the A section with a small variation in the final bar.

Bar 32 | *Eighth notes*
The final bar consists of four eighth notes. This rhythm was also used in the intro, but as the root note (C) is used here there is a sense of finality to the piece.

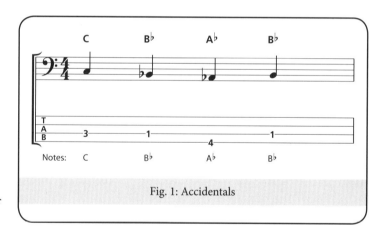

Fig. 1: Accidentals

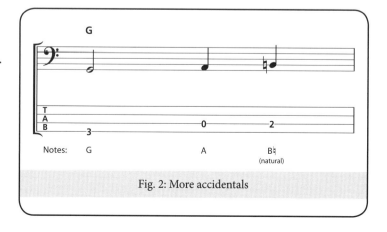

Fig. 2: More accidentals

Technical Exercises

In this section the examiner will ask you to play a selection of exercises drawn from each of the three groups shown below. Groups A and B contain examples of the scales and arpeggios you can use when playing the pieces. In Group C you will be asked to prepare the bassline riff exercise and play it to the backing track in the exam. You do not need to memorise the exercises (and can use the book in the exam) but the examiner will be looking for the speed of your response. The examiner will also give credit for the level of your musicality.

Groups A and B should be prepared on the starting notes of E, A and G. Before you start the section you will be asked whether you would like to play the exercises along with the click or hear a single bar of click before you commence the test. The tempo is ♩ = 70.

Group A: Scales

1. Major scale (A major scale shown)

2. Minor pentatonic scale (E minor pentatonic scale shown)

3. Natural minor scale (G natural minor scale shown)

4. Major pentatonic scale (E major pentatonic scale shown)

Group B: Arpeggios

One octave and should be played both ascending and descending

1. Major arpeggio (G major arpeggio shown)

2. Minor arpeggio (A minor arpeggio shown)

Group C: Riff

In the exam you will be asked to play the following riff to a backing track. The riff shown in bar 1 should be played in the same shape in bars 2–4. The root note of the pattern to be played is shown in the music in each of the subsequent three bars. The tempo is ♩ = 70.

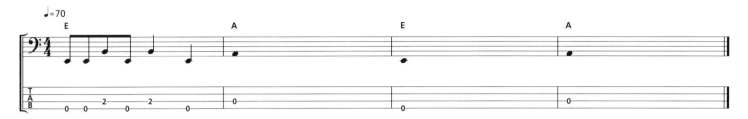

Sight Reading

In this section you have a choice between either a sight reading test or an improvisation and interpretation test (see facing page). You will be asked to prepare a sight reading test which will be given to you by the examiner. The test is a four bar melody in the key of A minor. The examiner will allow you 90 seconds to prepare it and will set the tempo for you. The tempo is ♩=70.

Improvisation & Interpretation

You will be asked to play an improvised bassline to a backing track of four bars in the keys of either C major or A minor. You have 30 seconds to prepare then you will be allowed to practise during the first playing of the backing track before playing it to the examiner on the second playing of the backing track. This test is continuous with a one bar count-in at the beginning and after the practice session. The tempo is ♩ = 70–80.

Ear Tests

There are two ear tests in this grade. The examiner will play each test to you twice. You will find one example of each type of test printed below.

Test 1: Melodic Recall
The examiner will play you three notes in sequence. You will identify whether the notes are higher or lower (up or down) in sequence. You will hear the test twice.

Each time the test is played it is preceded by a one bar vocal count-in. The tempo is ♩ = 85.

Candidate may answer either: "higher/lower" or "up/down".

Test 2: Rhythmic Recall
The examiner will play you a two bar rhythm played to a drum backing on the E string. You will hear the test twice. You will be asked to play the rhythm back. You will then be asked to identify the rhythm from two printed examples shown to you.

Each time the test is played it is preceded by a one bar count-in. There will be a short gap for you to practise. Next you will hear a vocal count-in and you will then play the rhythm to the drum backing. The tempo is ♩ = 90.

General Musicianship Questions

In this part of the exam you will be asked five questions. Four of these questions will be about general music knowledge and the fifth question will be asked about your instrument.

Music Knowledge

The examiner will ask you four music knowledge questions based on a piece of music that you have played in the exam. You will nominate the piece of music about which the questions will be asked.

In Grade 1, you will be asked to identify:

- The bass clef

- The time signature

- Whole, half, quarter and eighth note values

- The difference between a major and minor chord

Instrument Knowledge

The examiner will also ask you one question regarding your instrument.

In Grade 1 you will be asked to identify:

- The following parts of your bass – neck, fretboard, body, tuning-pegs, pick-ups and bridge

- One main bass make other than that of the bass you are playing

- Names of the open strings

Further Information

Tips on how to approach this part of this exam can be found in the *Syllabus Guide* for bass, the Rockschool *Bass Companion Guide* and on the Rockschool website: *www.rockschool.co.uk.*

Entering Rockschool Exams

Entering a Rockschool exam is easy. You may enter either online at *www.rockschool.co.uk* or by downloading and filling in an exam entry form. Information on current exam fees can be obtained from Rockschool online or by calling +44 (0)845 460 4747.

- You should enter for your exam when you feel ready.

- You may enter for any one of the three examination periods shown below with their closing dates:

EXAMINATION PERIODS

PERIOD	DURATION	CLOSING DATE
Period A	1st February to 31st March	1st December
Period B	1st May to 31st July	1st April
Period C	23rd October to 15th December	1st October

These dates apply from 1st September 2012 until further notice

- The full Rockschool examination terms and conditions can be downloaded from our website. The information shown below is a summary.

- Please complete your entry with the information required. Fill in the type and level of exam and instrument, along with the examination period and year. Paper entry forms should be sent with a cheque or postal order (payable to Rockschool Ltd) to the address shown on the entry form. Entry forms sent by post will be acknowledged either by letter or email, while all entries made online will automatically be acknowledged by email.

- Applications received after the expiry of the closing date, whether made by post or online, may be accepted subject to the payment of a late fee.

- Rockschool will allocate your exam to a specific centre and you will receive notification of the exam showing a date, location and time, as well as advice on what to bring to the centre. We endeavour to give you four weeks notice ahead of your exam date.

- You should inform Rockschool of any cancellations or alterations to the schedule as soon as you can because it may not be possible to transfer entries from one centre, or one period, to another without the payment of an additional fee.

- Please bring your music book and CD to the exam. You may use photocopied music if this helps you avoid awkward page turns. The examiner will sign each book during each examination. Please note, you may be barred from taking an exam if you use someone else's music.

- You should aim to arrive for your exam 15 minutes before the time stated on the schedule. Guitarists and bass players should get ready to enter the exam room by taking their instrument from its case and tuning up. This will help with the smooth running of each exam day.

- Each Grade 1 exam is scheduled to last 20 minutes. You can use a small proportion of this time to set up and check the sound levels.

- You will receive a copy of the examiner's marksheet two to three weeks after the exam. If you have passed you will also receive a Rockschool certificate of achievement.

Bass Grade 1 Marking Schemes

ELEMENT	PASS	MERIT	DISTINCTION
Performance Piece 1	12–14 out of 20	15–17 out of 20	18+ out of 20
Performance Piece 2	12–14 out of 20	15–17 out of 20	18+ out of 20
Performance Piece 3	12–14 out of 20	15–17 out of 20	18+ out of 20
Technical Exercises	9–10 out of 15	11–12 out of 15	13+ out of 15
Either **Sight Reading** *or* **Improvisation & Interpretation**	6 out of 10	7–8 out of 10	9+ out of 10
Ear Tests	6 out of 10	7–8 out of 10	9+ out of 10
General Musicianship Questions	3 out of 5	4 out of 5	5 out of 5
TOTAL MARKS	60%+	74%+	90%+

ELEMENT	PASS	MERIT	DISTINCTION
Performance Piece 1	12–14 out of 20	15–17 out of 20	18+ out of 20
Performance Piece 2	12–14 out of 20	15–17 out of 20	18+ out of 20
Performance Piece 3	12–14 out of 20	15–17 out of 20	18+ out of 20
Performance Piece 4	12–14 out of 20	15–17 out of 20	18+ out of 20
Performance Piece 5	12–14 out of 20	15–17 out of 20	18+ out of 20
TOTAL MARKS	60%+	75%+	90%+

Bass Guitar Notation Explained

THE MUSICAL STAVE shows pitches and rhythms and is divided by lines into bars. Pitches are named after the first seven letters of the alphabet.

TABLATURE graphically represents the bass guitar fingerboard. Each horizontal line represents a string, and each number represents a fret.

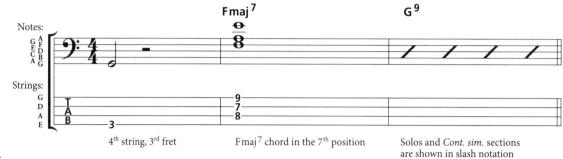

4th string, 3rd fret

Fmaj7 chord in the 7th position

Solos and *Cont. sim.* sections are shown in slash notation

Definitions For Special Bass Guitar Notation

HAMMER ON: Pick the lower note, then sound the higher note by fretting it without picking.

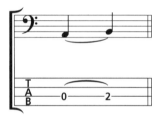

PULL OFF: Pick the higher note then sound the lower note by lifting the finger without picking.

SLIDE: Pick the first note and slide to the next. If the line connects (as below) the second note *is not* repicked.

GLISSANDO: Slide off of a note at the end of its rhythmic value. The note that follows *is* repicked.

SLAP STYLE: Slap bass technique is indicated through the letters T (thumb) and P (pull).

TAPPING: Sound note by tapping the string – circles denote a picking hand tap, squares a fretting hand tap.

DEAD (GHOST) NOTES: Pick the string while the note is muted with the fretting hand.

NATURAL HARMONICS: Lightly touch the string above the indicated fret then pick to sound a harmonic.

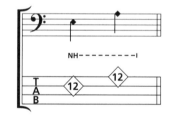

 (accent) ▪ Accentuate note (play it louder).

 (staccato) ▪ Shorten time value of note.

 ▪ Fermata (Pause)

D.%. al Coda

▪ Go back to the sign (%), then play until the bar marked **To Coda** ⊕ then skip to the section marked ⊕ **Coda**.

D.C. al Fine

▪ Go back to the beginning of the song and play until the bar marked **Fine** (end).

▪ Repeat bars between signs.

▪ When a repeated section has different endings, play the first ending only the first time and the second ending only the second time.

SONG TITLE:	MIDNIGHT MIST
GENRE:	HIP HOP
TEMPO:	100 BPM
KEY:	B MINOR

TECH FEATURES:	LONG NOTES
	CONSISTENCY
	OPEN STRINGS

COMPOSER:	NEEL DHORAJIWALA

PERSONNEL:	NEEL DHORAJIWALA (PROD)
	HENRY THOMAS (BASS)

OVERVIEW

'Midnight Mist' is a hip hop piece that recalls the work of contemporary, multimillion selling hip hop and rap artists including Kanye West, Jay Z and Dr. Dre. As with the majority of hip hop tracks, the bassline featured is simple but it is one of the most crucial elements of the song. This bassline features a lot of repetition, but also many subtle fills that add variety to the repeated chord progression. Being able to play long, consistent notes with a great feel is much harder than it seems, but this is the secret to playing this line perfectly.

STYLE FOCUS

Hip hop music is, and always has been, predominantly about the groove within the song. With that in mind, it is crucial that your bass part locks in tightly with the rhythm track of 'Midnight Mist'. Most hip hop tracks are built on one, two or four bar loops, and while the bassline is not repeated during the song, the chordal foundation is a looped two bar progression. The bass part here is all played in the lower register, so you will need to aim for a bass-heavy tone in order to mimic the well-rounded bass sound that can be heard on some of the mainstream modern hip hop songs.

THE BIGGER PICTURE

Hip hop began in New York in the 1970s as a cultural movement that encompassed music, dance and street art. The first hip hop track is generally considered to be 'Rappers Delight' by the Sugarhill Gang (1979), which reused the groove from Chic's disco hit 'Good Times' but with rapped vocals. Hip hop has evolved continuously since then by embracing new technologies. Drum machines and samplers have been key to the genre since the mid 1980s. Hip hop artists Kanye West and Jay Z have become renowned not only for their ability to write hits, but for their production skills too.

RECOMMENDED LISTENING

Modern hip hop albums worthy of investigation include *The College Dropout* (2004) by Kanye West, *The Blueprint* (2001) by Jay Z, and *Watch The Throne* (2011), a collaboration album between West and Jay Z. Other notable modern hip hop artists include Gnarls Barkley and The Roots. Gnarls Barkley is a collaboration between singer Cee Lo Green and producer Danger Mouse that yielded the 2006 hit album *St. Elsewhere*. The Roots are a live band who combine hip hop, jazz and neo soul. Their album *Phrenology* of 2002 is one of their finest.

Midnight Mist (Grade 2 Preview)

Neel Dhorajiwala

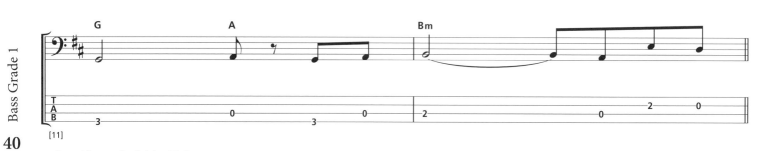

Bass Grade 1

40

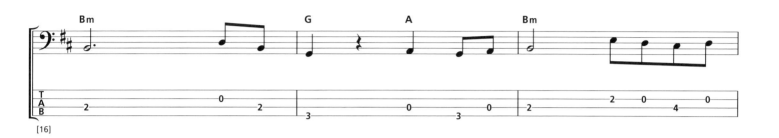

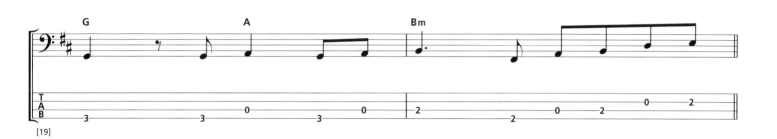

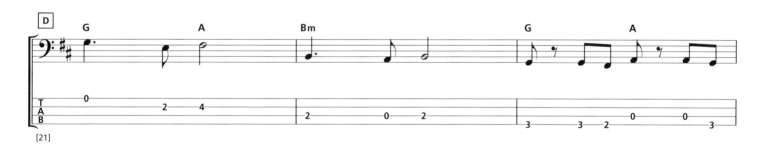

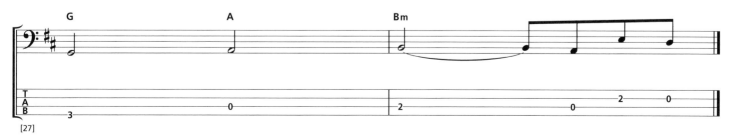

Bass Grade 1

Walkthrough (Grade 2 Preview)

A Section (Bars 1–4)
The first section of this song sets the mood and establishes the repeating two-bar chord progression. The bass plays a simple part here.

Bars 1–2 | *Approaches to the chord progression*
The first four bars demonstrate two ways to approach the same chord progression in a simple way. In the first bar, half notes are played under the G and A chords; you will notice that an E is played beneath the A (Fig. 1). This note is the fifth of the chord, not the root, and sounds highly effective in this instance. In the second bar, an F♯ is played under the Bm chord. This note is also the fifth of the chord. In bars 3 and 4 simple root notes are used instead.

Bar 1 | *Half notes*
In the first bar, two half notes are played. You should allow these to ring for their full duration: that is, two beats each. Try to let these flow smoothly into each other with no gaps between them.

B Section (Bars 5–12)
In this part of the song, the bassline becomes more active and demonstrates more varied ways to play in a supportive manner around the chord progression.

Bar 5 | *Dotted quarter note rhythms*
The first note of bar 5 is a dotted quarter note. Dots added after a note add 50 per cent. of their value again so this note should last for a beat and a half. The second note of the bar, E, should therefore be played on the '&' of beat two. This rhythm is common in all styles of music.

Bar 9 | *Rests*
In this bar, a simple quarter note rhythm is played with notes on beats one and three, and rests on beats two and four. Listen closely to the drum part here and ensure that both of your notes stop cleanly at the end of their respective beats. You should then hear the snare hits in the gaps.

Bar 12 | *Ties and eighth notes*
In this bar, a tie is used to allow the first note to last for two full beats and half of beat three (Fig. 2). The second note, an open A, is then played on the upbeat of beat three, followed by two further eighth notes. You should play the first note, counting the beats as you go, then play three even eighth notes starting on the '&' of beat three.

C Section (Bars 13–20)
The C section features a more active bassline that uses melodic hooks and lots of string crossing. Timing and accuracy are an important part of this section.

Bar 14 | *Open strings*
A phrase consisting of four eighth notes is used in the second half of this bar. Open strings need to be muted correctly for this line to sound as it should. After playing the first two notes of the phrase (the second is an open D string), your fretting hand should rest against the D string to stop it ringing. The C♯ on the A string is then played, followed by the open D string again. The last thing you want here is the open D to ring while you are playing the C♯.

D Section (Bars 21–28)
The bass moves back to simpler rhythms. There are more inversions, too, where non-root notes are played by the bass.

Bar 24 | *Dotted half note*
This bar features just one note (a B) played as a dotted half note. A half note lasts for half a bar, or two beats, and adding the dot means that it will last for 50 per cent. of its value again, making a total of three beats. Ensure that this note lasts for the full three beats with a rest on the fourth beat.

Bar 28 | *Ending*
The song ends on a sequence of three eighth notes beginning on the upbeat of beat three. This phrase has been used several times in the song and has always led back to a G chord in the next bar. This does not happen here, however, giving the ending of the song an unresolved feel.

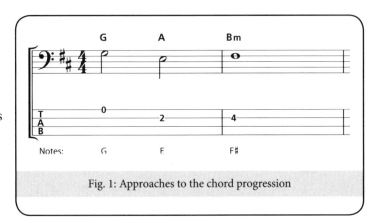

Fig. 1: Approaches to the chord progression

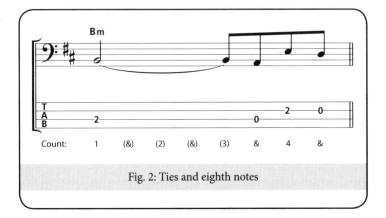

Fig. 2: Ties and eighth notes